JOHANN CHRISTIAN BACH

CONCERTO

for Harpsichord and Strings
für Cembalo und Streicher
E♭ major/Es-Dur/Mi♭ majeur

Edited by/Herausgegeben von
Ernst Praetorius

Ernst Eulenburg Ltd
London · Mainz · Madrid · New York · Paris · Tokyo · Toronto · Zürich

		Pag.
I.	**Allegro** di molto	1
II.	**Adagio**	19
III.	**Allegro con spirito**	26

All rights reserved. No part of this publication may be reproduced, stored in a retrieval system, or transmitted in any form or by any means, electronic, mechanical, photocopying, recording or otherwise, without the prior written permission of Ernst Eulenburg Ltd., 48 Great Marlborough Street, London W1V 2BN.

Revisionsbericht.

Als Vorlage dienten Stimmen mit folgendem Aufdruck:

Concerto I per il Clavicembalo
Due Violini,
Viola
e
Basso
dal
Sign. Giovani Christiano Bach
In Riga
Presso Giovani Federico Hartknoch.
(1770)

Es handelt sich hier um das erste der zwei bei Hartknoch erschienenen Konzerte (Nr. II 1772).

Beide Konzerte liegen zwischen den Berliner Frühwerken und den unter op. 1 bei Welcker in London erschienenen 6 Concerti pour le Clavecin. Der Form nach ähneln sie noch den Berliner Konzerten, sonst aber wird in ihnen der Einfluß der Mailänder Atmosphäre und des Studiums der italienischen Meister bereits deutlich. Bach war 1754 nach Mailand übergesiedelt, fand in dem Cavaliere Litta einen vorbildlichen Mäzen und wurde Schüler des Padre Martini in Bologna. Das vorliegende Konzert dürfte also etwa 1754/55 entstanden sein. Wie Schökel (H. P. Schökel: Joh. Christian Bach und die Instrumentalmusik seiner Zeit) ganz richtig bemerkt, entwickelt sich aus den „Motiven" der Frühwerke hier erstmals das „kantabile Allegrothema" resp. das „Thema" überhaupt.

Während die Berliner Kompositionen noch stark unter dem Einfluß von Ph. E. Bach, dem Lehrer Joh. Christians, stehen, wird in diesen ersten Mailänder Werken der Schüler selbständig, er tastet sich, wenn auch zunächst vorsichtig, auf dem Wege zur kompositorischen Freiheit vorwärts und schreibt dieses im eigentlichen Sinne „erste Originalwerk".

Vom Herausgeber wurden folgende offensichtliche Notenfehler korrigiert:

I. Satz: Takt 110 Vl. II: d statt es; Takt 126 3. Viertel: es, c, g, es statt g, es, c, g; Takt 159 Cembalo Baß: es, g, c, d, es statt es, g, c, f, g. —

II. Satz: Takt 62 2. Viertel: d statt cis. —

Sämtliche Zutaten des Herausgebers (mit Ausnahme der ausgesetzten bezifferten Bässe) sind durch Einklammerung resp. kleineren Stich kenntlich gemacht.

Er hofft, daß diese „Neuerscheinung" vòr allem praktischen Wert erzielt und in den Konzertprogrammen einen ihrem Wert entsprechenden Platz einnimmt.

Februar 1937.

Dr. Ernst Praetorius.

Revision Details

The original used for this print had the title :

Concerto I per il Clavicembalo
Due Violini,
Viola
e
Basso
dal
Sign. Giovani Christiano Bach
In Riga
Presso Giovani Federico Hartknoch
(1770)

This is the first of the two Concertos published by Hartknoch (No. II 1772).

Both Concertos belong between the Berlin early works and the 6 Concerti published as Op. 1 by Welcker of London. Formally they still resemble the Berlin Concertos, but otherwise the influence of the Milanese atmosphere and of the study of the Italian masters becomes apparent. Bach had removed to Milan in 1754, where he found an ideal promoter in the Cavaliere Litta and became a student of Padre Martini, Bologna. This Concerto is therefore likely to have its origin in 1754/5. As remarked by P. H. Schökel, *Joh. Christian Bach und die Instrumentalmusik seiner Zeit*, there develops for the first time from the "motives" of the early works the Theme Allegro cantabile resp. the symphonic "Theme" as such.

While the Berlin compositions still show a strong influence of Ph. E. Bach, J. Christian's teacher, the student becomes independent in these first Milanese works, he feels himself advancing on the way to freedom of style and writes this virtually first original work.

The following evident faults were corrected by the editor :

1. Movement : Bar 110 VI.II d for eb; bar 126 3rd crotchet eb,c,g,eb for g,eb,c,g; bar 159 Cemb. bass c,d for f,g.

2. Movement: Bar 62 2nd crotchet d for c.

All additions of the editor (apart from the realised figured bass) are made clear by brackets and smaller print.

He trusts this "new publication" will have practical value and assume a place in the concert programmes in accordance with its importance.

Dr. Ernst Praetorius.

Concerto

I.

Joh. Christian Bach
1735–1782

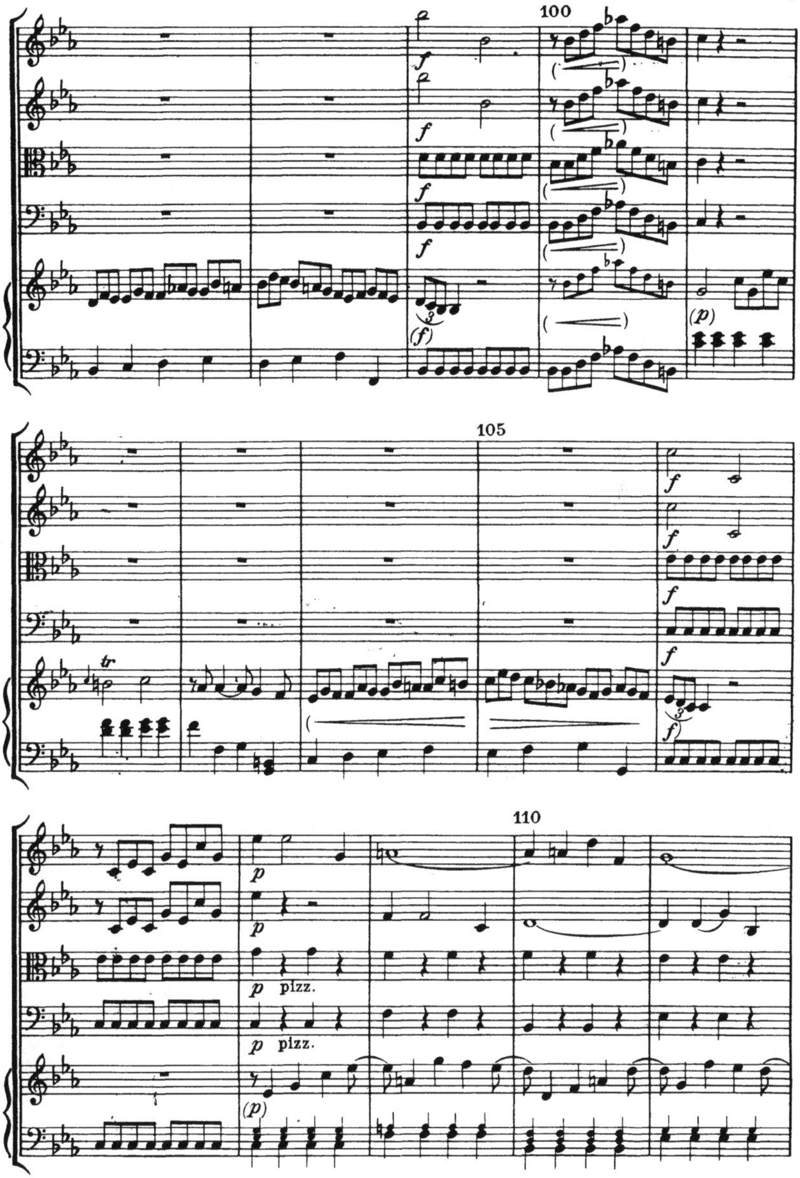
100
f
(f)
(p)
105
tr
110
p
pizz.
(p)

II.

III

Allegro con spirito

27

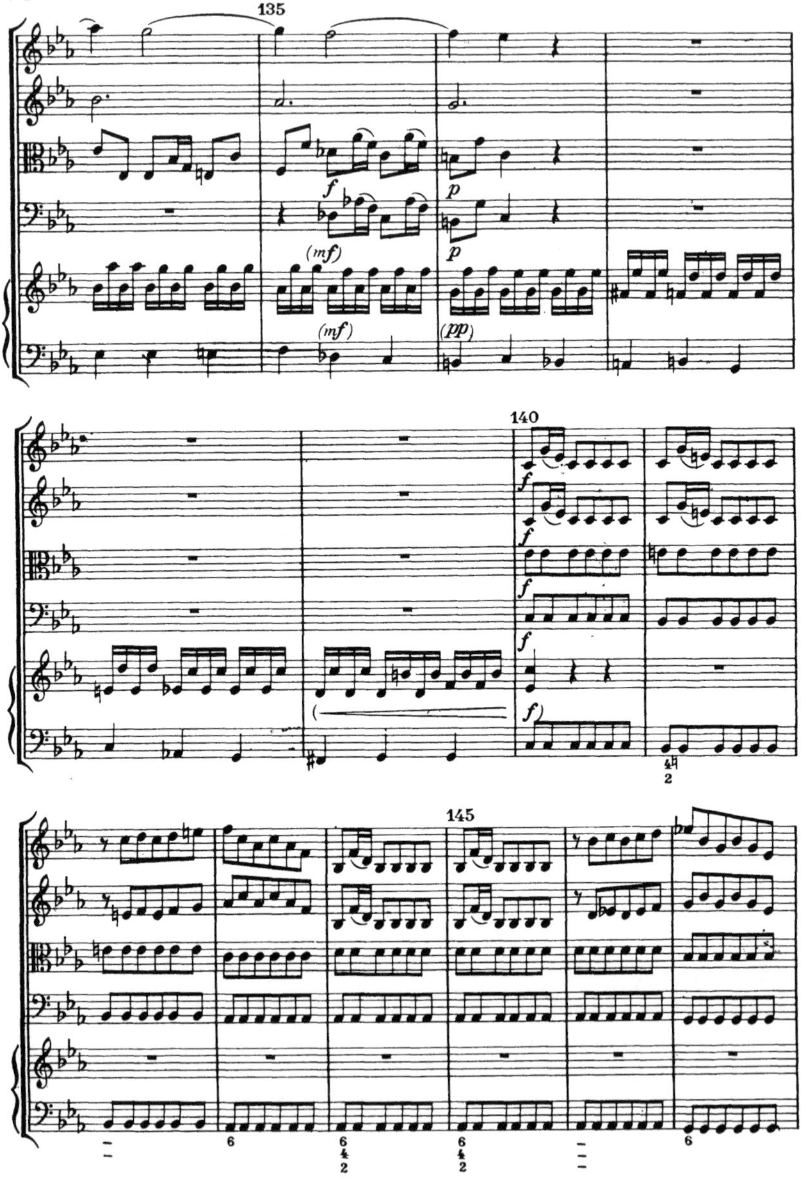
135
140
145

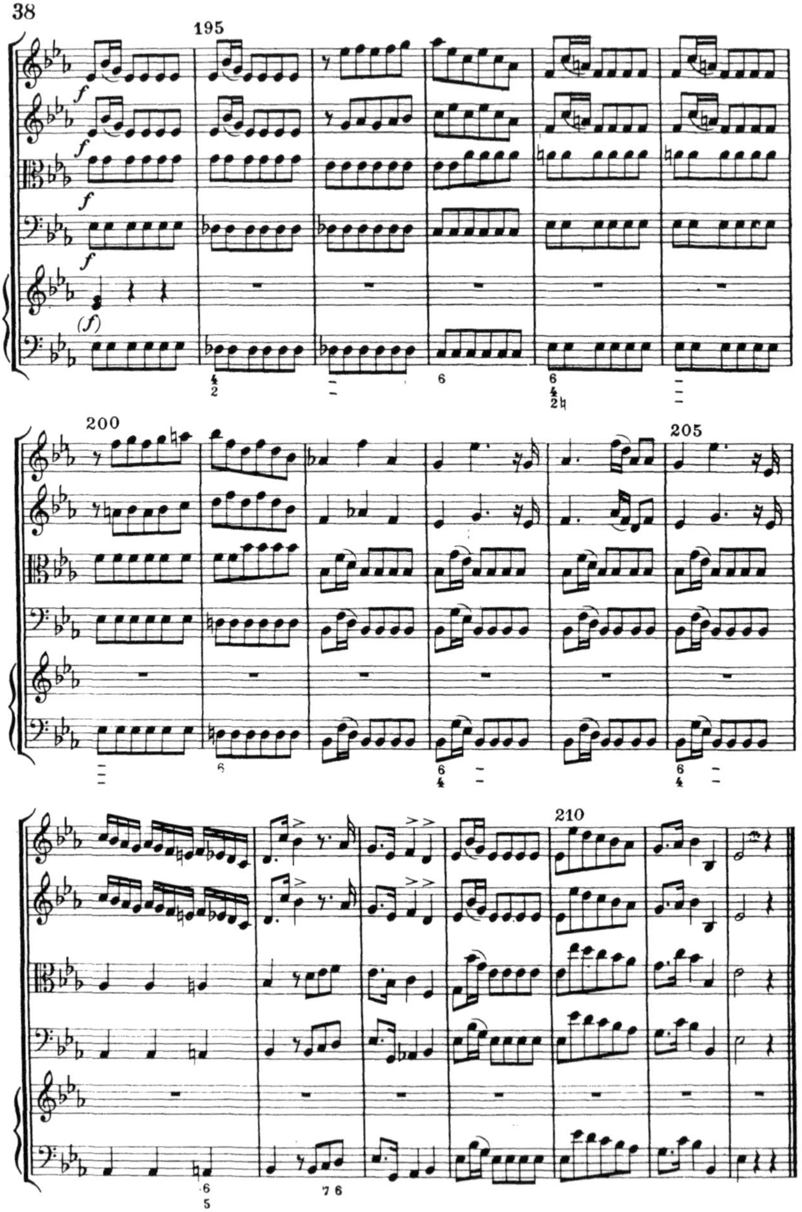
195
f
f
f
f
(f)
200
205
210